I am circling around God, around the ancient tower,
and I have been circling for a thousand years,
and I still don't know if I am a falcon, or a storm,
or a great song.

Rainer Maria Rilke

Sex is just the beginning, not the end.
But if you miss the beginning,
you will miss the end also.

Osho

SACRED ORGASMS

Teachings from the Heart

by

Kenneth Ray Stubbs, Ph.D.

illustrations
by
Kyle Spencer

Larkspur, California

Published by   Secret Garden
                      P.O. Box 67- SCA
                      Larkspur, California 94977– 0067

Illustrations: Kyle Spencer
Cover Photo: Jim Dennis
Author's Photo: Jim Dennis

ISBN 0-939263-07-6
Library of Congress Card # 91-62590

Also by Kenneth Ray Stubbs, Ph.D.

Romantic Interludes: A Sensuous Lovers Guide
Erotic Massage: The Touch of Love

WARNING

All the sexual positions, rituals, and activities in this book are not for every body. Some of the
          positions were accomplished only after years of yogic practice.
Because of the absurdity of the litigation-happy times in which we live, here is the seemingly
          necessary legal disclaimer:
          The author, illustrator, and publisher shall have neither liability nor responsibility to any
          person or entity with respect to any loss, damage, injury, or ailment caused or alleged
          to be caused directly or indirectly by the information or lack of information in this book.
So take responsibility for your own health. Please don't get stuck in a position you can't get out of.

Table of Contents

Dedicated to
my teachers
of sacred energy

Tarthang Tulku

Billie Hobart

Harley SwiftDeer

A Special Acknowledgment to
Jeannie Kruger
without whom this book
would not be
what it became

Sources

These are the authors and teachers who have had a major influence on what I wrote in *Sacred Orgasms*.

TANTRA

    Tarthang Tulku, a Tibetan Lama, guided me to a deep understanding of meditation, though he spoke of sexuality only once in my presence.

    Jwala, an American tantrika who walks her talk, confirmed my image of the maithuna ritual.

    Ralph Metzner, Ph.D., in *Maps of Consciousness* was the first to present, for me, a clear picture of tantra.

TAOISM

    Stephen T. Chang, M.D., Ph.D., author of *The Tao of Sexology*, through his seminars, books, and friendship, has taught me much about Taoism.

    The *I Ching*, by Richard Wilhelm, translated by Cary F. Baynes, would be the one book if I could keep only one.

QUODOUSHKA

    Harley SwiftDeer Reagan, Ph.D., a true warrior in many senses of the word, is a Cherokee shaman making available the Quodoushka teachings to those who are willing to take the leap. Diane Nightbird and Stephanie Wadel have greatly enhanced my understanding of these teachings.

    Some of the description/wording comes from SwiftDeer's training manual, *The Sweet Medicine Sundance Teachings of the Chuluaqui-Quodoushka*, copyrighted by The Deer Tribe Metis-Medicine Society and used with permission.

ENERGY

    Billie Hobart, in my first seminar with her, led me in a guided meditation focusing on an energy center above my head. When my awareness touched the center, tears came, and I felt I had *come home*.

WESTERN SEXOLOGY/EROTOLOGY

    The Institute for the Advanced Study of Human Sexuality in San Francisco provided me with teaching and learning opportunities unparalleled in any other contemporary academic setting. I am especially grateful to Clark Taylor, Ph.D., Laird Sutton, Ph.D., Marguerite Rubenstein, Ph.D., Ted McIlvenna, Ph.D., and Wardell Pomeroy, Ph.D..

Acknowledgments

Kyle Spencer illustrated the beauty of human expression perfectly for this book. She and her art are special more than she realizes.

Sandy Trupp, my publicist and friend, inspires me continuously.

Chyrelle D. Chasen is always there to support.

Jim Dennis—it was a joyful experience co-creating the cover photograph.

Deborah Harvey and Rick van Genderen were involved in the art and design of this book in so many, supportive ways.

Even while the chief justice of the U.S. Supreme Court was condemning public nudity as "evil," there were several conscious souls willing to celebrate their bodies for the illustrations. I am deeply grateful to Arline Bloom, Barbara Kaplan, Cheryl Myers, Connor Cockran, Deena Andrews, Dove Star, Louise-Andrée Saulnier, Steve Brown, Ray Langerin, Ren Zaugg, Thomas Tong, and Wendell Carter.

After completing most of the new paradigm, for clarification/collaboration/refutation I consulted with several clairvoyants/metaphysicians/metapsychologists/dowsers: Carolyn Parker, Foster Perry, Jeannie Kruger, Luisa Murphy, Lynn Ryckman, Patricia-Rochelle Diegel, Ph.D., and Richard Feather Anderson. They indeed cannot be blamed for any erroneous perspectives on my part.

Several dear friends and professionals gave extensive editorial feedback: Burt Cutler, Christopher Murphy, Clara Kerns, Kathleen Hughes, Laird Sutton, Ph.D., Nadine Stefanov, Sandy Trupp.

My appreciation likewise goes to several others who contributed in different, special ways: Annie Sprinkle, Cliff Peterson, Jimmy Scott, Ph.D., Maria Silva, Stan Russell, Ph.D., and all the people who over the years told about their out–of–the–ordinary orgasms.

The Illustrations

The illustrations of the sexual positions/rituals are based on photographs.

My original idea was to have contemporary couples demonstrate the sexual positions described/ depicted in the traditional texts/sculptures/paintings/teachings. As the photographic sessions evolved, it became apparent that the relationship/pleasure/joy between the two people in the illustration is far more important than the historical correctness of the position/ ritual.

So, some of the positions are the couples' favorite positions, some are the couples' playful interpretations/adaptations of depictions/descriptions from books or from instructions of teachers of these traditions, and some are the couples' spontaneous creations during the photographic sessions.

The personal instructions came from Harley SwiftDeer and Jwala. The inspiring depictions/ descriptions were in these books: *Ecstasy Through Tantra* by Dr. Jonn Mumford, *The Eastern Way of Love* by Kamala Devi, *Sexual Secrets* by Nik Douglas and Penny Slinger, and *The Tao of Sexology* by Dr. Stephen T. Chang. The genital reflexology illustrations are based on very similar illustrations in *The Tao of Sexology* and used with permission.

Section I: CONTEMPORARY SEXUALITY

1.   The Spirit and The Flesh

Intercourse and orgasm:
     that's what sex is

Of course, sex is more than intercourse and orgasm
     But this is what most of us think/do/say
          most of our sexual time

There is nothing wrong with
     just intercourse (or any consensual sexual actions)
          and orgasm
     Most of us—not all of us
          would be healthier and happier
          if we did more
          sex
                    consensually
                    with others and/or ourself
          and orgasm

But there is something terribly *wrong*
     It is not really wrong
     It is *wrong*
If we have grown up in Western culture
     which is basically Christian culture
     with various threads
     of various philosophies and various theologies
               such as Greek philosophy and Judaism
     woven in
we have, most of us
     in our world view, our cosmology, our psyche
     in our core
a basic *wrong*

The *wrong* is *not*
     that *spirit* is different than *body*
               Concepts allow differentiation
               Differentiation can bring us to the wonder
                         of it all
                    the incredible, magnificent complexity
                         of it all
The *wrong*
     is that *spirit* is sacred and
               body is profane
     The spirit is spiritual, the body is flesh
          One is of heaven, the other is of sin

We've got it all wrong

Both are sacred

And orgasm teaches us that

Love beds are altars. People are temples
encountering temples, the holy of holies
receiving the holy of holies.
Matthew Fox, *The Coming of the Cosmic Christ*

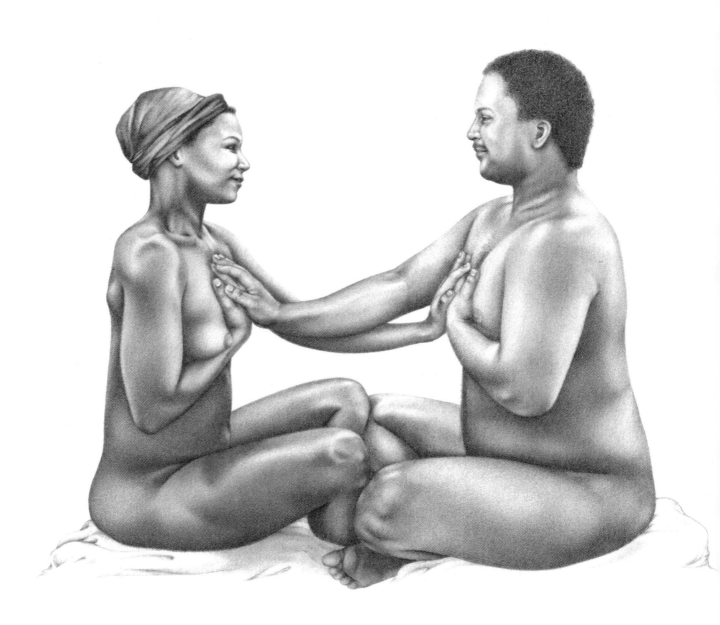

Even if we understand this—that both are sacred
    it may take a lifetime, a long time, a short time
to live it

However, it takes no *time* to experience it
In orgasm
    we go outside of time
    we go outside of location
    we go outside of identity
        outside of mind
    we transcend concept, language
    In orgasm, there is
        no right/wrong
        no good/bad
        no spiritual/evil

Then after orgasm
    we, most of us most of the time,
settle back into the profane

After orgasm
    we revel in the orgasm
    we savor it
        luxuriate in it
        classify it
        compare it
        demean it
        depreciate it
        hope for it again
        try for it again
        crave for it again
        or just roll over and fall asleep

If we have never had orgasm
    or
if we think we have never had orgasm
    we can fake it
        read about it
        hope for it
        be afraid of it
        ache for it
            and not know why we ache
        work on it

Sacred Orgasms, the book, is *not* about
    how to have/achieve/reach orgasm
    it is not about *mature* orgasms
        or multiple orgasms
    it is not about how not to *lose* an erection
        how not to ejaculate too soon
        how not to ejaculate with an orgasm
            (for those who can and don't want to)
        how to ejaculate
            (for those who can't and want to)

Sacred Orgasms is about shifting the paradigm
    about stepping outside our framework
    about stepping into a different *reality*

a *reality* that still is conceptual
thus, still limits us
because any paradigm
is a conceptual framework

The paradigm in *Sacred Orgasms*
holds both the spirit and the body
as sacred
Likewise, both are profane
if we choose to live our life that way

Religious teachings
most of them most of the time
hold the spirit as sacred and
the flesh as profane
Though through the ages
mysticism has sometimes
expressed reverence
for the marriage of the body and the soul
occuring during the *ecstatic experience*

Scientific teachings,
having themselves attained a religious fervor
most of the time,
hold matter as profane
Thus, the body is profane
(though miraculous)
The spirit, if measurable,
would be profane
as well

Sexology
is the interdisciplinary study of sexuality
especially human sexuality
Being principally scientific, this field of study
views the body as profane
most of the time:
how often we do it
intercourse, other sex actions, orgasm
with whom
with what
when
how to do it
how not to do it
how to do it better
From sexology,
an immense amount of information
and a valuable set of therapeutic procedures
are bringing us—some of us
out of a millennium or two of
sexual suppression
sexual repression
sexual oppression
slowly, awkwardly sometimes
Probably there is no other way out

There is another -ology
    Named after the ancient Greek god of love,
        Eros, whom later the Romans called Cupid,
erotology
    is the study of sexual pleasure,
        of lovemaking rituals
    It is the study of the representations of our sexual nature
        in sculpture, in paintings, in music, in film, in literature
    This -ology, unfortunately, is more of a coined term
        than an extensive field of study
    Here, usually, there is a reverence
        for the body
        for the senses
        a recognition of love
    Spirit is affirmed, some of the time,
        though the emphasis is physical

Contemporary sexuality, however,
    is more what it is
    more,
    probably,
    because of the artist
Artists, many of them much of the time,
    are outside
        outside of the mainstream
        outside of the power structures
        outside of the cultural embargoes
    the dancer, the musician, the singer,
        the actor/actress express
    the sculptor, the painter, the filmmaker reveal
    the poet, the songwriter, the writer remind us of
        our soul
        our beauty
        our passion
        our joy
        our love
        our wonder
    Artists
        far more than the high priest/esses
            of religion and of science
        have liberated
            celebrated
            proclaimed
            consecrated
                the spirit and the body

When we interweave these institutions
        with a myriad of other patterns
    we have *contemporary sex*,
        which for most of us most of the time looks like this:
Subject: one person
            or
      two people physically together
        female/male, male/male, female/female
Verb: to have sexual actions
        usually with the genitals

Even as fire from stone and iron springs,
From soul and body leaps the spark divine
Mahmud Shabistari, *The Secret Garden*

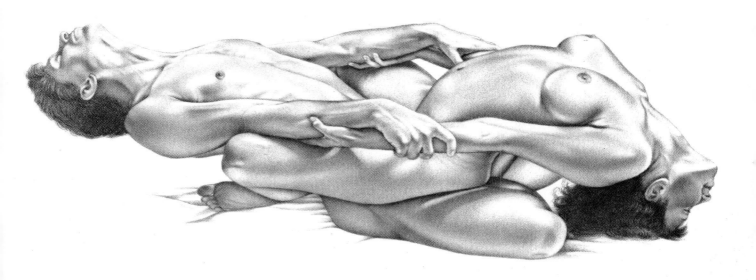

often with the mouth and/or hands
usually on one or more of these:
clitoris, head of penis,
G-spot, prostate gland
Object: orgasm
hoping for multiple orgasms
hoping for mutual orgasms
if there are two people
Adverbs and Adjectives—such as *gentle, tenderly, passionately*:
this is the language
of lovemaking and romance

There are many variations to these patterns
for some of us *some* of the time
for some of us *most* of the time
It's simply a matter of choice
and there are lots of choices

2.   Safer Sex

Just say No!
and many variations on the theme

This is what organized religions and governments
often with admonition incurring guilt and shame
sometimes, often
have advocated, propagated, ordered,
extorted, imposed, invoked

All
that is necessary for *just say no*
is
to be ignorant

The *just* in *just say no* means
we do not need any information
other than the slogan

Pure ignorance
when bodies feel sexual pleasure
—here ignorance is bliss
there is no mind
to censure
to censor
When bodies sexually interact physically
there may be the possibility
of transmission of pathogens
(harmful microorganisms)
and/or
the creation of unwanted, uncared-for offspring
—here ignorance is stupidity

After penicillin
After *the pill*
we

many of us
    sometimes
broke loose
Some of us became tri-sexual
    I'll try anything—at least once
Just say yes was bliss

But medical science has not saved us
    Sex is faster

If the pathogen is not called
            one of the current names
    there will be another pathogen
            with another name
    more or less harmful

If we are sexually active with another
    and most of us will be
            sooner or later
            (*sexually active* here means sexually interactive
                at least once)
we basically have two options:

Be ignorant
    or
Take responsibility

In the heat of passion
    remaining ignorant is the easiest
    Just do it and hope everything is OK in the end

How to take responsibility
    depends on the circumstances

Saying *no* for the moment
    may be the best choice
But don't *just* say no
    Get information

The information may be
    from medical and public health sources
    from alternative health sources
    from other sources
Each of us must choose for ourselves
    which sources are
    reliable and relevant

Some of the information may come
    from our sexual partner or partners
            with reciprocity on our own part
Sexual secrecy, when it comes to physical health,
    serves no one
Honest communication is essential
    what we have done
    what we want
    what we do not want

Once we have information on what, when, how

—information which may or may not be complete,
          which may or may not be totally accurate
we choose
          what to do and
          what not to do

If our partner's choice is different
     we negotiate
There may not be a consensus
     To discontinue interaction is also a choice

By choosing, we are taking responsibility
     for our physical, mental, emotional, and spiritual well-being

Information
Communication
Choice
     These are my personal guidelines for safer sex
          I have not always followed them
          I probably will not always follow them
               even though I wish I would
     Your guidelines are yours to choose and follow

Once the Wheel of Love
has been set in motion,
there is no absolute rule.
Kama Sutra

Section II: FOUR TRADITIONS

3.   Out-of-the-Ordinary Orgasms

Orgasm
    in contemporary Western sexology
    and for most of us personally most of the time
basically is
    muscular tension release

(Definitely, though,
    not all tension releases
    are orgasms)

This is the pattern:
    A build up of muscular tension (myotonia)
            and tumescence (vasocongestion, engorgement of blood)
            often with body movements accompanying
    An orgasm may follow:
            a series of involuntary muscular contractions
            in the pelvic floor
            producing
                    in the male, often though not always
                            an ejaculation of fluid
                            out through the urethra
                    in the female, sometimes
                                    but not for most, most of the time
                            an ejaculation of fluid
                            out through the urethra
    Finally, a general release of muscular tension occurs

Multiple orgasms basically means that
    instead of a more-or-less complete release
            of muscular tension
    another cycle begins with tension buildup
            followed by involuntary pelvic-floor contractions
            followed by a general release of muscular tension
    This can continue for a period of time
            with an ejaculation during none, some, or all
                    of the series of pelvic-floor contractions

There is, of course, more to orgasm than physiological phases:
    feelings
    emotions
    intense experiences
    an altered state of consciousness
These usually are only verbally reported to
            the scientific researchers
    not measured directly by
            the scientific researchers
Thus, our model of orgasm
    is what science defines/describes:
    basically, physical tension release

It is a valuable model, a useful model
Orgasm as a series of physiological changes
            is an excellent way to frame / think of
      what many of us experience most of the time
            when we have sex
            with others, with ourself
It's the some-of-the-other times
            the some-of-the-other experiences
            the some-of-the-other orgasms
            the mystical ones
      that aren't explained by / understood from
            a physiological definition

Sometimes, even if there is a
            tension/contractions/release cycle,
      this is only incidental to the totality
            of the experience
Or
      the context is non-sexual and/or
      the activity is non-sexual
Or
      something about the experience
      does not
            look/smell/taste/feel/sound like
      the textbook definitions of sex and orgasm

Some of these experiences are once-in-a-lifetime occurrences
      —a sort of cosmic orgasm choosing us
Some have been consciously repeated
Some have been consciously attempted
      often to remain only *attempted*

The list of *out-of-the-ordinary orgasms*,
            a term for a diverse spectrum of experiences,
      is long
Here are only a few
            without genital stimulation that I have
            experienced, heard about, and/or read about
                  (though out-of-the-ordinary orgasms
                        can definitely occur
                        with genital stimulation as well):

      while listening to *Tristan and Isolde*
            by Wagner

      while smelling a night-blooming jasmine

      while climbing a rope

      while taking the first bite of a peach

      while receiving a massage
            between the toes
            on the thighs
            on the abdomen
            around the ears

        on the left triceps muscle
        on the back of the neck

while *giving* a massage
        on the back of the neck

while doing breathing exercises

while only fantasizing

while watching someone teach, fully clothed,
        how to do *meditative sex*

while meditating quietly

while videotaping a space shuttle blast off
        when the rumble of the bass sound waves hit

while watching waves crashing on the rocks
        for half an hour

while skydiving, immediately after jumping out of a plane
        for the first time

while watching dolphins
        swimming/leaping in the water

while embracing non-sexually

while lying beside someone chanting

while running the shower on shoulder muscles

while reading the manuscript of this book

while touching the wetness of a tomato plant

while riding on buses, on subways
        feeling the vibrations in the pelvis

while hugging a tree

while lying on a large rock
        just *feeling* the energy of the rock

while having a chiropractic adjustment
        in the lower back

Once a friend bluntly explained that
        St. Teresa of Avila's *ecstatic, mystical communions* with God
            really were orgasms
        (St. Teresa was a sixteenth century nun
            who, during the Spanish Inquisition,
            wrote about her spiritual life)
        "Sex with God," I thought
            "What a way to keep celibacy vows!"

Your body is the harp of your soul,
And it is yours to bring forth sweet music
from it or confused sounds.
Kahlil Gibran, *The Prophet*

Another friend tells of making love with his partner
    Both are suddenly looking *down*
        at a couple below, on a blanket on the grass
           just like themselves
    Then they realize
        it is themselves
           they later report to each other

Others tell of dreams
    vivid dreams
    where they are having orgasms
        in the dream *and* in their physical body
    In the dream they are making love
        with their partner
        with someone they do not know
        with energies without definite form
        with water flowing around their pelvis and
           through their legs
In one vivid dream a person is being led toward *The Light*,
    a massive, continuous, orgasmic explosion

While watching television, a friend's pelvis
        began to move, until he had an orgasm
    Looking around at the rest of his family
        he realized no one else had had the same experience
        from the TV
    He was only two years old

Several friends have exclaimed
    they have experienced orgasms
        while giving birth
        while breast feeding

Religious services are not excluded:
It was a hot, humid Sunday morning church service
    with hand-held fans barely lifting the air
    when I saw a congregation member *get happy*
        as it is sometimes called
This was no somber religious gathering
The preacher, as the high priest/ess is termed there,
    was giving a sermon building in fervor
    while various members of the congregation
        responded vocally
        in rhythm
        to the preacher's invocation
           of the Holy Spirit
           as well as the human spirit
The whole church broke out in hymn
    hands clapping
    the organ and the piano pounding a primordial beat
    voices lifted in praise
As the religious passions escalated
    one of the several congregation members
        dressed in all-white in the front pew
    became even more expressive than the others
Her arms and torso movement appeared to become uncontrollable
    her singing converted to moaning screams

As a novice to such gatherings, I had been forewarned
    by my friend who nodded to me
    that the woman was OK
    as she collapsed to the floor
        her body vibrating and proclaiming itself
Several of her all-white-clad companions swiftly moved
    over to her assistance and fanned her
After a while, while others continued singing,
    she was raised back to her seat in the pew
She was more than OK—she had *gotten happy*
    She was in spiritual ecstasy

A few years later I reflected
        somewhat seriously, somewhat jokingly
    getting happy is an orgasm
        intense, expressive, communal
        with the Holy Spirit perhaps
        with herself
        I don't know
    but still an orgasm

Another few years later
    while reading the Kinsey report
        on sexual behavior in the human male
    I read basically the same description of orgasm
        as *getting happy*
    It, however, was not about
        church-service experiences
        It was a description
        of orgasms in infants

Another friend reminisces of her *spiritual master* in India
    He would sit in meditation
        with a small gathering of followers
    After a while, their bodies would
        vibrate, undulate, shake…
        eventually slump/jump/writhe/swoon
            to the floor *in bliss*
        only to be carried away by attendants
    so that the next soon-to-be-orgasmic group
        could be escorted in
    There was no sex, as most of us would call it
    The spiritual teacher was *making love*
        with energy
        without touching an *erogenous zone*

Whenever there is a paradigm shift
    there is a turning point
        a catalytic event
    when the *cognitive dissonance* is too dissonant
        and we let go of the reigning
            concepts, definitions, framework
    If we believe the world is flat
        but we have just sailed west continuously
            and have returned to our starting point
            without falling off the world

we might change
                    our concept that the world is flat
          Here is my turning point:

It was late one evening while I was working in my office
Feeling that something was different
          that there had been an energy change
          I sat down in meditation
First I sensed the *presence* of a new friend
          We had met on a business phone call a month earlier
                    and though we had never been face-to-face,
                    several phone conversations had established
                             a beginning friendship
          Even if it were not my friend
                    I felt I could trust the presence
          and so *relaxed* into the energies near me
Within about a few seconds
          my breathing expanded
                    in sigh-like movements
A gentle but definite
          flow of energy lifted up from my head
          to a foot or two above me
Then everything was calm
Though I had had
          no sexual feelings, no erection, no ejaculation
          I suddenly thought, "She just had an orgasm."
It was late in the evening
          even later three thousand miles east
                    at my friend's home
          but she had said it was OK to phone late
My first words: "Did you just have an orgasm?"
She burst out laughing as she said, "Yes."
          (The phone call was not an interruption
                    as she was alone)
My friend has more psychic abilities
          than most people I know
          but to send/project/present her energy
          three thousand miles away...

This had *not* been a mystical dream
                    a theoretical fantasy
                    a delusion of ecstasy
          The exact person, the exact time, the exact event
          All totally verified

More was to come
In the following months
          mutual orgasms with my long-distance friend began to occur
                    mutual three thousand miles apart
In the middle of the night
          sleeping alone and apart from each other
          when we awoke in orgasm
                    we would check our clocks
In a morning phone call
          the orgasm times were verified as the same
                    with adjustments for time zone differences
Intensely "pleasurable sexual orgasms"

Through a tremendous outpouring of psychic energy in total devotion and worship for this other person, who is respectively god or goddess, you realize by total fusion and contact, the divine center in them. At once it bounces back to you and you discover your own.

Alan Watts, *Play to Live*

was her description
For me: an electric-shock-like sensation
throughout my energy field
with my physical body whipping across the bed
Pleasurable, non-sexual, no erection, no ejaculation
but *orgasm* is the only word I would use
While this was the turning point,
the long-distance orgasms
turned out to be only the beginning
of my journey to a new paradigm

It was a hot summer evening
even hotter because the windows were closed
so as not to awaken the neighbors again
as a friend / lover / meditation partner and I
were having good ole contemporary sex
the coital kind, of a safer-sex, condom-sex variety
though not in the missionary position
We had begun with quiet meditation
back to back, breathing in unison
then some massage and caressing
Somewhere along the way
our bodies flowed into intercourse
There was no rush,
though, indeed, there was sweat and passion
At some point my orgasm began
with the usual
pelvic-floor contractions and
ejaculation
as my partner went into her orgasm
which in her usual, contemporary-sex fashion
was long and intense
Shortly my own orgasm completed
Then, unanticipated, a few seconds later
my back and neck began to arch
with my mouth stretching open
and the sounds of orgasm erupting again
through my chest and throat
joining my partner's screams
as she continued in orgasm

Everything was just like
my orgasm of a few moments earlier—except
there were
no pelvic-floor contractions
no ejaculation
This was an orgasm that felt just like a sexual orgasm
in every way and everywhere
except in my pelvis
It was as if my partner's core
was pulling me up into her explosion
up into one, encompassing, merged, energetic orgasm
One thing for certain though,
even the closed windows
did not keep the neighborhood quiet that night

Neither this energetic orgasm

nor the earlier long-distance mutual orgasms
were to be anything like an experience a year later
I was visiting a desert area
noted for its *power spots*, or *energy vortexes*
This is a place where Native Americans came for ceremony
where stone cathedral formations
spire toward the heavens
where boulders aeons ago came to rest on buttes
giving them the appearance of
birds, lizards, other animals,
and mythical beings
It is called *sacred earth* there
and so a Catholic chapel had been constructed
framed around a magnificent, tall cross
facing the south
But the sacred earth was to be found, for me,
outside
several yards to the east
and here it was I came to meditate on several afternoons
Each time, to find the place
for that afternoon's meditation
I would from inside myself
feel the earth
This time I selected the middle of three tiers
where ancient waters had carved Rubenesque beauty
into the red-toned stone
Sitting down
with my legs dangling over a ledge
I closed my eyes
and began my usual inner observation of sensations
in and around my body
Almost immediately my back began to arch
I had felt energy in this desert area before
but this time it was particularly intense
and so I leaned back
allowing the warm stone to cradle me
There, before I could even become surprised,
a blast of light and sound surged into my head
blinding my senses
for only a moment maybe, I am not certain
Maybe it was like the light that blinded Paul
as he journeyed through the desert
on the way to Damascus
All I remember next
was a sound inside my head,
a sound which seemed to be
the humming roar of the light
in the center of my brain
There was no up or down
as I came back to consciousness
only the movement of my legs dangling
and my hands
searching for gravity
bracing the stone

I had felt a surge not unlike a sexual orgasm
except that the explosion was in my head

somewhere in the center of my consciousness
Though there were
no sexual feelings, no erection, no ejaculation
again, the experience was pleasurable
again, my best description is *orgasm*

While these experiences
with my long-distance friend
the energetic orgasm following the sexual orgasm
and the Earthgasm
were not consciously attempted or sought after
they did not occur in a vacuum
There had been many years of conscious *seeking*
There had to be more meaning to existence
than what I had felt/seen/heard/learned
in church and in school

Many teachers and many teachings
from other traditions and
from outside mainstream culture
have been sought / discovered / bumped into
along my path
Without these teachers and teachings
there would not have been a paradigm shift, probably
The descriptions, the interpretations
of the teachings
that follow
are mine
These are my
over-generalizations
over-simplifications
often personal reinterpretations
of teachings
I have read, heard, and/or experienced
What makes these teachings different
than mainstream thinking
is that *spiritual* and *sexual* are not in opposition
The spirit and the body
are integral parts of wholeness
where *atonement* is replaced by *at-one-ment*

4. Tantra

Tantra (pronounced *tahn´ trah*)
today in the Western world
has come to mean
spiritual sexuality
Indeed, *tantra* has almost become the generic term
for all styles/traditions of spiritual/meditative sexuality

Tantra
which is part of both
some Hindu and some Buddhist teachings

(Union is) as if in a room
there were two large windows
through which the light streamed in:
it enters in different places
but it all becomes one.
St. Teresa of Avila, *Interior Castle*

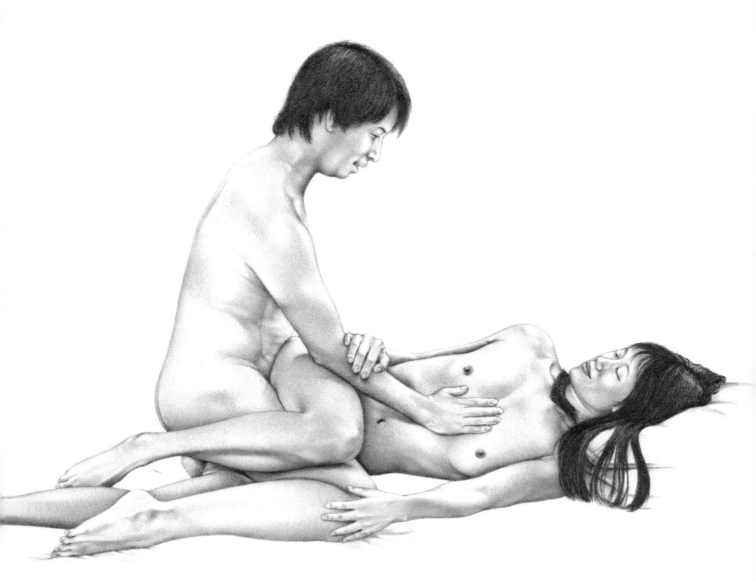

actually is far more encompassing
than *sex done spiritually*

Tantra embraces all:
    birth, death, pleasure, pain
    wealth, poverty, beauty, ugliness
    joy, sadness, anger, fear, ecstasy
    sex, celibacy
Tantra basically is a teaching of acceptance
    a teaching of non-attachment
        When we are *grasping* an object/action/outcome
            we are attached
            there is no freedom
        When we are *avoiding* an object/action/outcome
            we are attached
            there is no freedom
        It is through the acceptance of all
                as it is
            that we become/are free
            Acceptance
                is not submission
                is not giving up
                Here, acceptance means non-attachment

By embracing the present
    while letting go of
        expectations of the future and
        comparisons with the past
    we can fully dance with life
        (and death)
There is no good/bad
        no right/wrong
        no spiritual/evil
    only suffering
        unless/until we let go of our attachments

Neither being sexual nor being celibate
        is preferable
    If we feel superior/inferior because we are/aren't sexual,
        we are attached
    If we feel superior/inferior because we are/aren't celibate,
        we are attached
    If we feel superior/inferior when we do/don't masturbate,
        we are attached
    If we feel superior/inferior because we do/don't do
            heterosexual actions
            or homosexual actions
            or bisexual actions
        we are attached
    If we feel superior/inferior because we do/don't
            go to church/synagogue/the ashram/etc.
            pray/meditate
            tithe/donate
            or do any other religiously sanctioned action
        we are attached
There are other words for superior:
    pious, proud, arrogant, egotistic, patronizing, condescending

There are other words for inferior:
      guilt, shame, worthless, incompetent, unimportant
      dumb, awkward
It is neither in the doing-ness nor in the non-doing-ness
It is in how we relate to an object/action/outcome
      that makes the difference
If we are attached to an object/action/outcome,
      sooner or later we will be in
          physical/emotional pain/discomfort
    when the object is no longer there
        or is there when we don't want it there
    when the action is too slow, too fast, too...
    when the outcome is different than
      we had hoped/expected
sooner or later we will be in
      what the Buddha termed *dukkha*
        (pronounced *doo´ kah*)
      which is loosely translated as suffering

So, do we simply
    stop doing the bad behaviors?
    start doing the good behaviors?

The answer is not in the stopping or starting
    Rather, we shift how we relate
      to what we be/do/have
    We transform the grasping energy
    We transform the avoiding energy

How to transform energy?
    To find that answer, those answers
    is why some of us search the world
      for gurus
        or any other form of high priest/ess
    That is why some of us spend years
      sitting at a master's feet
    That is why some of us enter monasteries and convents

When we are able to
    transform/convert/transubstantiate/transmute the energy
      at will
    we are liberated
    we are enlightened
    we are in nirvana
    or in Christian terms
      we have entered the Kingdom of God / Queendom of Goddess

There are many paths
    to learn ways to transform energy
Sex is one of those paths

Sex is a path to liberation
Sex is a path to enlightenment
Sex is a path to the King/Queendom of God/dess

Sex is not the only path
    not the best path for all of us
      but definitely a powerful path

Here, though,
        sex is usually not the sex
                that most of us do most of the time
        Here, sex is not
                just the *contemporary sex* characterized earlier
A more accurate concept for sex
        intended to transform energy
                would be *meditative sex*
        Some would say *spiritual sex*
        Either term is suitable
                as long as we do not slip into a belief
                        that spiritual sex is superior to
                                flesh sex
                                base sex
                                friction sex
                                passionate sex
                                raw sex

Meditative sex has its varied forms
Contemporary sex has its varied forms
        Sometimes the forms look the same
                Sometimes the forms look very different

In many schools of tantra
        there are at least four major types of meditative forms:
                mantra (*mon´ trah*)
                mudra (*moo´ drah*) and asana (*ah´ sah nah*)
                pranayama (*prah nah yah´ mah*)
                yantra (*yawn´ trah*)

A mantra is a sound or series of sounds
                sometimes vocally produced
                sometimes silently imagined
                sometimes sounds from nature,
                        from musical instruments,
                        or other sources
        OM is the most noted
        Amen is similar in the West
        Likewise, The Lord's Prayer is a mantra
        Ummmm and *oooh* could be sexual mantras

A mudra is a body gesture or posture
                especially with the hands
An asana is specifically a body posture
        In meditations, gestures and postures
                are often combined
                Jesus is often depicted standing
                        with his arms, hands, and fingers
                        in definite positions
                The palms placed together while praying
                        is another mudra
                The Buddha sitting cross-legged is common
                        in the East
                Sexual positions can be asanas

Pranayama is conscious breathing in specific patterns
                Rapid inhalation and exhalation

Blow upon my garden,
    let its alluring perfumes pour forth
        Song of Songs

through the nostrils
is one of the more well-known Eastern forms
Sports training and singing training
often utilize certain breathing techniques
Sometimes Western sex therapy teaches
that holding our breath
inhibits the orgasm response—so breathe!

A yantra is a visual representation
often using geometric shapes
A yantra can be observed externally
or visualized internally
A mandala is a yantra with a circular motif
Symbols, colors, pictures, all can be yantras
The cross,
with the horizontal bar at different positions,
is common across cultures and across the ages
Botticelli's *Birth of Venus* is a renaissance yantra

Meditation, often,
simply
is doing a mantra, mudra/asana, pranayama,
and/or yantra
At least, this is what meditation looks like
These are the forms we often learn first

Actually,
meditation is the conscious
awareness/attentiveness/mindfulness
while we are doing the meditation forms

Actually,
meditation is the conscious
awareness/attentiveness/mindfulness
during every moment
regardless of the form/non-form
we are doing/not-doing
if we remain consciously aware

So what is meditative sex?

Here is one image, using tantric forms:
sitting cross-legged in coitus
with our sexual partner
while chanting OM
while gazing into our partner's left eye
It's that simple
—unless we have difficulty sitting cross-legged

While this is accurate, it is only the humorous answer

Compared to contemporary sex,
tantric sex is far more ceremonial
There are elaborate methods of
nurturing and stimulating the senses
expressing devotion
honoring the sacredness of sexual union

Such a tantric sex ritual,
 sometimes known as *maithuna*
  (pronounced *my thu´nah*),
 is at the other end of the spectrum
  than the *quickie*
 Though, in tantric philosophy,
   both would be sacred
  Maithuna is more intricate
   in time, intent, and activity

The forms, however, are not what make
 meditative sex meditative
It is the approach:
 the awareness
 the attentiveness
 the mindfulness
These make sex meditative
Being in the present
 being aware of sensations of skin touching skin
 tuning into the pressure building in our pelvis
  or elsewhere
 hearing the sound of our breath,
  our partner's breath
   if we are with another/others
 feeling our heart beat
 being mindful of the muscular tension building
All these
 without the past or the future
 And if our mind goes to the past, to the future
  we are even aware *also*
   of the past/future images/thoughts
All this is meditative sex
 regardless of the forms
 regardless of whether we are doing what we term
  masturbation, oral sex, anal sex,
  genital-genital sex, tantric sex rituals,
  or any other form of consensual sex

Some of us have been doing meditative sex all along
 at least to some degree
 at least some of the time

But to *understand* meditative sex
 is to understand part of the paradigm shift:
  we are more
  than a physical body
 Not *more* in the sense of
  mental, emotional, physical, spiritual aspects
 Rather, *more* in the sense
  that the physical body is only *one*
  of several systems

Tantric teachings hold that
 there are other
 coexisting, interacting systems
 that each of us has
  in varying degrees of development

Systems is my term
Some other terms are
    energies
    energy fields
    subtle bodies
    energy bodies
    light bodies

These other systems are *subtle*
    in the sense that
    the effects in the physical, material world
    are not obvious
        to most of us
        most of the time

The most commonly taught subtle energy system is
    the *chakras*
        (pronounced *shah´ kras*)
This is a system of energy centers
    often thought of as along an imaginary axis
        in the core of our physical body
      from the bottom of our pelvis
        (commonly called the *first chakra*)
      to the inside top of our head
        (commonly called the *seventh chakra*)
    Most schools of meditation teach that
      there are seven principal chakras
        along the imaginary axis
      with secondary chakras
        throughout the body,
        the number varying in different traditions

A clarification of our language:
    chakras are not *in* the physical body
      though a chakra's *location* can be conveniently identified
      by naming an area of our physical body

Chakras, in Sanskrit,
        means *wheels* or *discs*
    they have also been described as
      cone-shaped vortexes

More important, though, is their function:
    Chakras are often considered
      energy transformers
    Analogously to the physical body's
      digestion process transforming food,
    the chakras transform energies
      for us to utilize

Tantric meditations in general, usually, are designed
        to awaken
        to develop
        to utilize
    the energies and the functions

HIs cheeks are like beds of spice, treasures of ripe perfumes
His lips are red blossoms; they drip liquid myrrh
His arms are rods of gold
        his hands crystal olive branches...
His mouth is delicious, his whispers are dear,
        and his expressions, *"Desire"* itself

Song of Songs

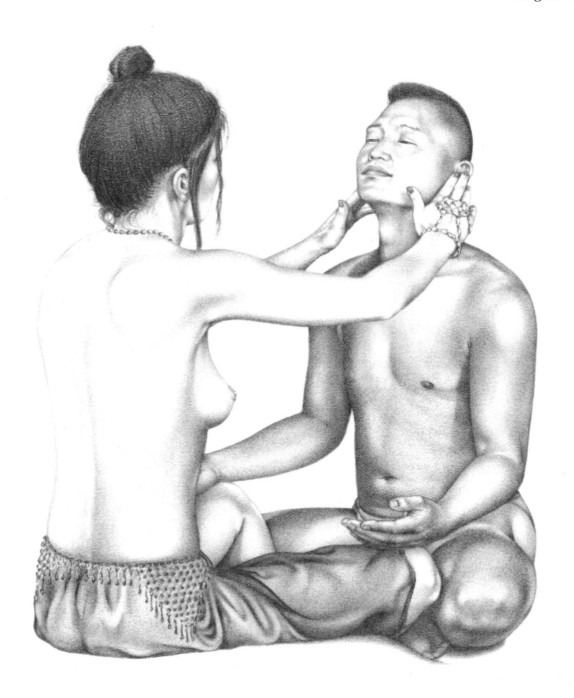

of the chakras and other subtle energy systems
Likewise, tantric sex rituals,
    and most other forms of meditative sex,
  are designed to do the same:
    to awaken
    to develop
    to utilize
  the energies and the functions
  of the chakras and other subtle energy
The conscious
    awareness/attentiveness/mindfulness
    are, in a sense,
    keys to the doors
      of these not-so-physical systems
      as well as the physical body system

Herein lies a fundamental contrast
  to the Western
    spirit-higher-than-the-flesh framework:
There is no denial of the physical body
    no subjugation
    no demeanment
Similarly, the physical body is
    neither idealized, glorified, nor idolized

In tantra,
  the extent to which
  the physical body and the subtle energy systems are
    attuned
    balanced
    centered
    coordinated
    integrated
    synchronized
    unified
  is the extent to which
    we can transform energy
  is the extent to which
    we can fulfill our potential

5. Taoism

T'ai Chi Ch'uan (pronounced *tie gee chowan*)
  is an ancient martial art
    with roots in Taoism,
    an ancient spiritual philosophy
      from China
    (Tao is pronounced *dow*)

When we observe the ritual,
  we see a slow-motion dance
    of flowing agility and keen balance

Once a master was in the middle

of the t'ai chi ch'uan ritual
A passing sparrow lighted on the swaying branch
          unaware
                    it was a floating hand
                              of the master
                                        effortlessly balanced upon the Earth
After resting,
          the sparrow was ready to continue flight
To gain the necessary momentum to begin flight
          the sparrow thrust off with its legs
However, the master
                    being very sensitive
          yielded to the force,
                    the hand descending
                    the exact distance, direction, and velocity
                    of the thrust
Without a resisting surface,
          the sparrow could not take flight

Recognizing the bird's desire to depart
          the master chose to steady the hand
                    offering the necessary resistance
                    for the sparrow's thrust
                              to flight
This is a story about
balance and yielding
          which are central in Taoism

Balance can be
          between Heaven, Human Being, and Earth
          between yin and yang
                    (pronounced *yen* and *yahng*)
          which could be translated as
                    receptive and active, respectively
          balance in the flow of energy
                    through the acupuncture meridians
          balance between the Five Elements
                    in traditional Chinese medicine:
                              fire, water, wood, metal, earth
          In Western concepts,
                    there would be a balance
                    between the mental, emotional, physical, spiritual

Yielding
          is characterized by the Chinese term *wu wei*
                    (pronounced *woo way*):
          allowing things to flow in accordance
                    with the nature of things
          Wu wei is noticeably similar
                    to the non-grasping and non-avoidance
                    of tantric philosophy
When we are in the river of life
          we can struggle paddling upstream
          we can hurry paddling downstream
          or we can *allow* the river
                    to carry us at its own pace
                    while we enjoy the scenery
                    along the way

In our quest for sex and orgasm,
    contemporary sex would look very different
    if we were to incorporate
        Taoist balance and yielding
    Sex, probably, would be
        less goal oriented
        less of a performance
    Sex, probably, would be
        slower
        longer
        more exploratory
        more sensual
        more intimate

Health and longevity
    also are central in Taoist thought
For us, as human beings,
    the extent to which
        we have health and longevity
    depends, greatly, on the extent to which
        we live in harmony
            with the changing seasons
            with social, political, and cultural changes
            with the cycles in the bodily functions
            with all change,
                which is basic to existence
To live in harmony with changes,
Taoism offers practical teachings:
    how to make wise decisions
    how to balance our diet
    which herbs to use and
    which acupuncture/acupressure points to stimulate/sedate
        to maintain and restore health
    which meditations to strengthen
        our internal organs and glands
    how to use sex and sexual energy
        to improve health, to harmonize relationships,
        and to increase spiritual realization

A Taoist teaching about The Seven Glands
    helps us to understand
    how sex and sexual energy
    are part of health and longevity
The seven glands in one of the classic texts are the
        pineal gland
        pituitary gland
        thyroid gland
        thymus
        pancreas
        adrenal glands, and
        the sex glands, here defined as
            in the male: the prostate and the testes
            in the female: the ovaries, uterus, vagina,
                and breasts

That the number of glands
    and the number of principal chakras

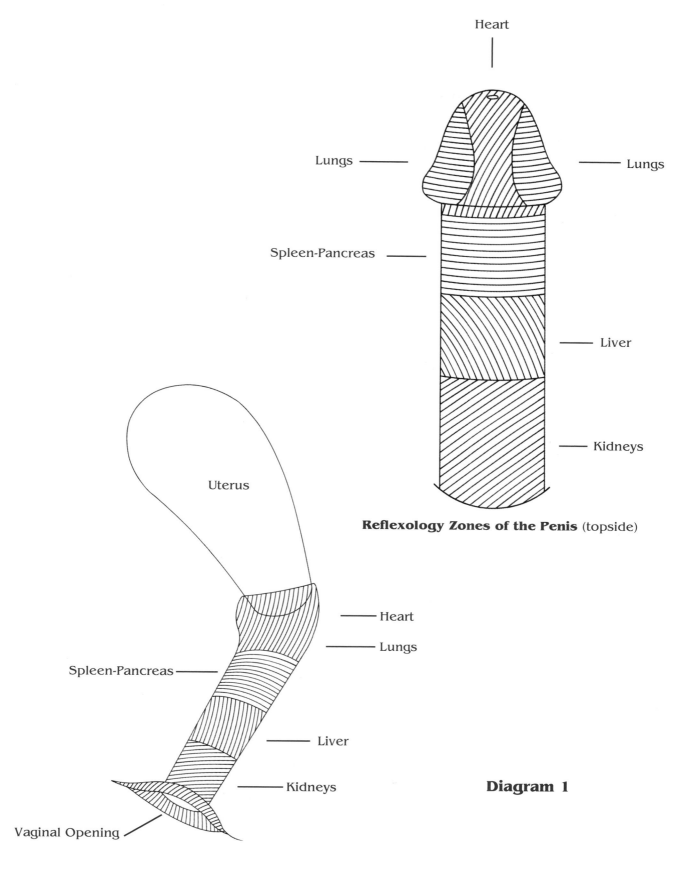

Heart

Lungs — — Lungs

Spleen-Pancreas —

Liver

Kidneys

Reflexology Zones of the Penis (topside)

Uterus

— Heart

— Lungs

Spleen-Pancreas —

Liver

Kidneys

Diagram 1

Vaginal Opening

Reflexology Zones of the Vagina

are the same
is more than coincidental
In the Taoist tradition,
            as well as other traditions,
        the glands and the chakras
        are viewed as
        functionally interdependent

In The Seven Glands teaching,
        which is more analogous
                than scientific,
        each gland is dependent (at least indirectly) on the others
                for its energy
        If a gland is excessively drained of its vitality,
                such as in an illness,
            all the other glands are drained
        If a gland has extra energy,
            all the other glands benefit

To increase the energy level
            of the glandular system
        there are various methods
One specifically for the *sex glands*
            is translated as The Deer Exercise
        Basically, this is
            the contraction (and later the relaxation)
            of the pelvic floor muscles
        In the tantric tradition, a similar method
                is called the mula bandha
                (pronounced *moo lah bahn' dah*)
        In the West, a similar method
                is called Kegel Exercises,
                or simply, Kegels,
                (pronounced *Kay' gulls*)
                named after a physician
                        who re-*invented* similar exercises

For many of us,
        sexual intercourse is
                a way to feel pleasure
                a way to express love
In Taoist teachings,
        sexual intercourse can also be
        a healing method
To understand coitus as a healing,
        it helps to understand the theory of reflexology
        In the West, foot reflexology already
                is a common massage form
        Here, different parts of the body
                    correspond to different parts of the foot
            By massaging or applying pressure on a place on the foot,
                    we can have a healing effect
                    on another part of the body
        For example, massaging certain places
                on the big toe
                can eliminate/reduce a headache,
                        according to the theory

and many peoples' experience
In Taoist teachings,
there is also a reflexology of the genitals
By having sexual intercourse in specific ways/positions,
certain organs are affected
such that a healing effect occurs
(See Diagram 1 for the organ systems on the genitals)
Personally, I know of no testimonials
supporting or refuting this healing theory
developed in ancient times
But it does sound like a wonderful way
to play doctor

To ejaculate or not to ejaculate
—that is the question
raised not only in Western sports training
In tantric approaches
some propose ejaculation
some propose non-ejaculation
Taoist teachings, however,
are a strong proponent of non-ejaculation
or at least of limiting the frequency
of ejaculation
Much nutritional energy is lost with each ejaculation
according to the Taoist teaching
so it would be better to learn
to have orgasm without ejaculation
or at least to have a
retrograde ejaculation,
which is when the ejaculate goes up into
the bladder
rather than out through
the urethra
A Taoist equivalent teaching for the female
is to minimize or to not have menstruation
through conscious, healthy meditative activities

For Taoists,
non-ejaculation and non-menstruation
are considered a central teaching
for those who wish health and longevity
Western medical science,
usually, would disagree

6.   Quodoushka

Many of us
who have felt/sensed/known/hoped
that sexuality is not in opposition
to spirituality
have turned to the East
to India, China, Tibet, Japan
for new teachings, different approaches

But such teachings were already here
in North America

though Native Americans had learned
for their own survival
not to talk about such teachings
in the presence
of oppressive armies
with oppressive moralities

Quodoushka
could be translated as
spiritual sexuality
The word itself comes from Native American Cherokee culture
(here pronounced *kwah doesh´ ka*)
and Mayan culture
(here pronounced *ka doesh´ ka*)
Some of the practices and concepts have
similarities with tantric and Taoist sexuality

In the Quodoushka tradition
children were taught from a young age
about the beauty of sexuality
about having reverence for sexual union
about honoring those with whom
we express our sexuality
At puberty, after the rites of passage
into adulthood,
the young adult would study
for several years
with a *fireperson*
the gender of whom depended on
the young adult's sexual orientation
A fireperson is a medicine man/woman
(a high priest/ess)
specialized in *fire-medicine*,
the ancient knowledge of spiritual sexuality
Their teachings included
what most of us would call
the physical art of lovemaking
one-to-one with the young adult
(The recently *discovered* G-spot, for example,
has been known for centuries
as *The Secret Fire-Trigger of the Serpent*)
Another major Quodoushka teaching was
how our sexual partner(s) are a mirror
of the different aspects of ourselves,
not at all unlike some of the current
Western psychological theories
However, very unlike what most of us
were ever taught
in school or in church/synagogue,
the young adult learned about
the chakras and other subtle energy systems
—directly, experientially
sometimes in solitude meditations
sometimes in sexual union with another

Move into the love act so deeply that the actor is no more.
While loving, become love; while caressing, become the
caress; while kissing, be the kiss.

Lord Shiva

In the Quodoushka tradition,
    the subtle energy systems
      are not just esoteric/hidden/secret teachings
        solely for the medicine person
    Development of the chakras, the aura, the shields,
        the luminous sphere
      and other translated terms for subtle energies
      was a standard part of education

In contrast to contemporary Western education,
    the Cherokee tradition teaches
    the sacredness of all existence
Before I was introduced
    to even the basics of Quodoushka teachings,
    the Cherokee shaman
      (another word for medicine person, high priest/ess)
    began with The Sacred Pipe Ceremony
After the stem and bowl were joined
    and the herbal mixture lit,
soon began the invocations to the
        powers/energies/essences/beauty
    of the Four Directions
        North
        East
        South
        West
    of the Five Worlds
      the sacred plants
        the Flowers
        the Trees
        the Grasses
        the Herbs and Shrubs
        the Teacher Plants
      the sacred animals
        the Four Leggeds
        the Winged Ones
        the Swimmers
        the Creepers and Crawlers
        the Mythological Animals
      the sacred humans
      the sacred minerals
        the Gems
        the Crystals
        the Sands
        the Rocks/Stones
        the Ores and Metals
      the sacred ancestor spirits
    the invocation to Grandfather Sun, Grandmother Earth
    the invocation to the Great Spirit, Wakantanka

In Biblical terms, the Sacred Pipe Ceremony said,
    "Be still and know that I am God"
My translation:
    "Be still and experience the sacred presence"

Only after this psychological/spiritual platform
    was laid

did the sensual and sexual instruction begin
Even the basic teaching tool
    is a sacred symbol:
            the wheel / the circle / the sacred hoop

On the wheel
    the positions are represented by the cardinal directions:
            North, East, South, West
    and the non-cardinals:
            Northeast, Southeast, Southwest, Northwest
Each of these positions has
    certain qualities/characteristics/meanings
    Almost any topic (it seems)
            such as sexuality, the seasons, colors, relationships
    can be examined/taught/appreciated
    from the diverse aspects of the positions
            around the wheel
The wheel,
            unlike most scientific linear thought,
    has no *beginning*, no *end*
    There are no superior places, no inferior places
            just different places, different viewing points
            each with its value and meaning
    A different position is a different experience
            in which we can *participate*
            if we choose

There is a wheel for different types of lovers:
        in the North: the Career/Goal-Oriented Lover
        in the East: the Temple Priest/ess Lover
        in the South: the Shy, Curious Lover
        in the Southwest: the Explorer/Adventurer Lover
        in the West: the Wanton/Lusty Lover
            and so on
Most of us, most of the time
    are *stuck* in one of these positions on the wheel
            we are unimaginative
            we are reluctant to leave our comfort zone
            we are socially conditioned as to what
                    the different genders *should* do,
                    the different roles we *should* play
The Quodoushka tradition teaches us
    to explore all the different personas
    on the wheel
The extent to which we recognize
    and realize in ourselves
            all of these sexual personas
    is the extent to which
            we have a full, balanced sexual life

This was but one of the teachings
            given by the Cherokee shaman
    before closing with the Sacred Pipe Ceremony
            to give thanks
            to all the powers/energies/essences/beauty
                    for being present and guiding us
                    during the sexual teachings

7.   Contemporary Meditation

The body is a temple
　　　　　for the spirit
　　This has long been a mystical tenet

The physical body is more than a tool
　　　　　　to accomplish physical tasks
　　It is more than a resting place
　　　　　for the mind
By being aware, by focusing
　　　　　on our physical sensations
　　　　　　　　whatever
　　　　　　　　wherever they are
　　we are more able to bring ourselves
　　　　　into the present
In this presence,
　　　　is where
　　　　we are more likely to find
　　　　　　our spiritual dimensions

It is incredibly simple:
　　we quieten the mind
　　　　　by placing our awareness on the physical
　　and we touch the spiritual
　　　　　which brings us back,
　　　　　　　if it is truly spiritual
　　　　　　　rather than a lifeless morality,
　　　　to the meaning and the beauty
　　　　　　of physical existence

Returning to the spirit
　　by being attentive to the physical
　　has taken several forms
　　　　　for me personally:
　　t'ai chi ch'uan
　　yoga
　　sitting crosslegged, chanting for hours
　　　　　with a Tibetan lama
　　　　　　　Om Ah Hum Vajra Guru Padme Siddhi Hum
　　　　　　　Om Ah Ra Pa Tsa Na Dhi
　　　　　　　Om Mani Padme Hum
　　observing silence in Catholic monasteries
　　　　　during four a.m. ceremonies
　　　　　smelling the frankincense and myrrh
　　　　　feeling the vibrations of the chords
　　　　　　in the Gregorian chants from the monks
But more than these
　　　　it was human touch
　　　　　　that brought me back most
　　　　　　to my spiritual dimension

A formal name for human touch is
　　　　　massage
Massage, actually, usually, at least for me,
　　　　is a two-person meditation

You are an enclosed garden
with a secret fountain
Song of Songs

Learning to give and to receive massage
is a training in being present:
our hands touch the body
we allow our body to be touched
with awareness
with attentiveness
with mindfulness
It was here
in the study of massage
that I discovered/evolved
my own, personal,
contemporary form of meditation

Massage is a dance
between two
—one active, one receptive
Giving massage, truly giving
is like sculpturing:
smoothing away the rough edges
to allow the beauty within
to be revealed
Receiving massage, truly receiving
is opening ourselves
to experience
the totality of our self
This is the meditation of, the art of massage

Massage is ancient
The forms are varied
What makes them *massage*
is the patterned touch
The patterns
usually are done with the hands
sometimes with the feet
occasionally with the elbows or knees
occasionally with other parts of the body
The patterns can be
deep, firm
light, delicate
vigorous, intense
gentle, subtle
slow, still
rapid, quick
The emphasis can be on the
skin
muscles
fascia which surround the muscles
internal organs
joints
blood circulation
lymph circulation
pressure points
energy fields
within and/or exterior to the physical body
The intent can be
more physical, such as
to reduce muscular tension

           to assist tissue healing
           to detoxify, to cleanse
      more psychological/emotional, such as
           to open up, to release
                  blocked/repressed/suppressed feelings of
                      sadness
                      contentment
                      fearfulness
                      anger
                      joy
                      sexual arousal

Many massage forms
    have other names than *massage*:
            acupressure, bodywork, deep tissue massage,
            reflexology, chiropractic, applied kinesiology, rolfing,
            laying on of hands, sensual massage, etc.
    many are forms from other centuries, other cultures
    many are current developments/modifications/adaptations
    many are so synthesized
            they constitute
            a new, contemporary cultural form themselves
but all are basically
    one person touching another
    in patterned methods
            usually, potentially,
                with awareness
                with attentiveness
                with mindfulness

As a meditation, massage brings us
    into direct contact
    with each other's
            mind/body/spirit/emotion
Two people open themselves, potentially,
    to intimacy
    to a common union, to communion
    to a depth of emotional connection
            that can be experienced
                only—usually
            when making love:
                vulnerability
                sensitivity
                respect
                appreciation
                merging together energetically
The only real difference
    between a massage and making love
    is that massage,
            as it is taught most of the time
                in professional trainings and in personal growth classes,
    does not involve
            genital touching and orgasm, intentionally

In my professional massage training
    I learned a donut massage
            —there was a hole in the middle

physically and emotionally
Massage techniques were taught
for every part of the exterior physical body
except for *down there*
between the legs
(Most massage schools exclude female breasts,
some exclude the buttocks,
some exclude even more)
All human feelings/emotions were accepted:
if there are tears, good, let them flow
release the sadness
if there is anger, good,
pound on pillows
express it through sounds in your voice
release the suppressed emotion
All human feelings/emotions were accepted
except for one, basic, primary one:
sexual

But sooner or later,
if we touch other human beings
personally and/or professionally
we will have choices to make
regarding sexual feelings
choices about
how to respond to others' sexual feelings/emotions
when and how to express our own sexual feelings/emotions

Most of us, most of the time
make an unconscious choice: we suppress

However, to the extent that we suppress/repress/deny/demean
our emotional dimensions
is the extent to which
we limit our spiritual dimensions

Moreover, the more we suppress/repress/deny/demean
our emotional dimensions,
the more likely that
suppressed emotions
will be expressed in abusive ways

Somewhere along the way
most of us came to a belief, a decision
that the only option to
sexual suppression/control
is
uncontrollable, animalistic desire/passion/lust
There *are* more options, more conscious choices
This is what the tantric, Taoist, and Quodoushka teachings
as well as massage
are about:
the transformation of energy
of physical energy
of emotional energy
of mental energy
of spiritual energy

You want to travel with her
You want to travel blind
and you know that you can trust her
for she's touched your perfect body
with her mind
             Leonard Cohen, *Suzanne*

For me personally
it was the meditation of massage
more than any other form
that brought me face-to-face
with my sexuality
Every time I gave or received
a massage,
the potential for sexual feelings
was there
The more powerful, the more impactful the massage,
the more the potential
regardless of the other's
gender, age, physical appearance,
or nature of our relationship
This is where I learned most
how to transform the energy of sexual feelings,
and thus to be more in conscious choice

Section III: ENERGY

8.   Signposts

What we don't need is another
  dogma
  or another rigid belief system
      to become attached to
      to defend
      to attack
      to be politically correct about
      to create a religious group around
Dogmas and other rigid belief systems
      limit us ·
  they have all the answers
  we no longer question them
  we no longer live our experience
      we live our beliefs, lifelessly
On the other hand, without conceptual frameworks,
      a multitude of events/experiences
      appear unrelated
  we don't see/feel/sense/hear
      the meaning of it all
Somewhere
      between dogma and meaning*less*ness
  there is
      meaning*ful*ness
My intent in presenting
      my interpretation
  of several traditional teachings
  is to share some of the signposts
      I've used
  to share some of the main frames
      in which I found meaning
The signposts may or may not be directions
          for each of us
Even with the signposts, though,
      there are, along the way,
          unpaved roads
          washed-out bridges
          quicksand
And probably
      the someone elses
          who put up the signposts
      didn't really understand
          where they had been anyway
      And sometimes
          the someone elses
          used the same term
              to mean different things/directions
      and very often
          different terms
          to mean the same things/directions

It all gets terribly confusing
        at times

But at least the signposts
        for me
    confirmed that someone else also
        had been seeking

Sacred Orgasms proposes
  a paradigm shift
      from the contemporary Western, scientific point of view
These are the central concepts:
    1. We are more than a physical body
    2. Orgasms are an energetic experience
        sometimes but not always with
        a physical tension/contractions/release cycle
    3. Our spiritual and our sexual dimensions
        are not only
            not in opposition,
        they are mutually enhancing

The conceptual framework/paradigm
      that follows
    embellishes these three ideas
The framework is
    my way of holding it all together,
    my way of understanding,
        of bringing meaning to
        some major, personal experiences
The framework
    may or may not be valid
        totally or partially
The framework
    is *not* an attempted synthesis
        of others'
        traditions, teachings, concepts, information
The framework is my own evolution
    continuing to evolve
It comes out of my own personal form of
    meditation/intuition/contemplation/sensing/experiencing
        though the concepts
        are strongly influenced by others'
            traditions, teachings, concepts, information
The framework is far more complex
        than it appears here
    There are many more functions than described
        and the structures vary
            depending on the circumstances
              and phases of development
The framework may appear to be static
        It definitely is not
    The descriptions
        are not always applicable to each of us
        during our many different
            possible phases of development
              (This is one of the reasons
                there are so many different

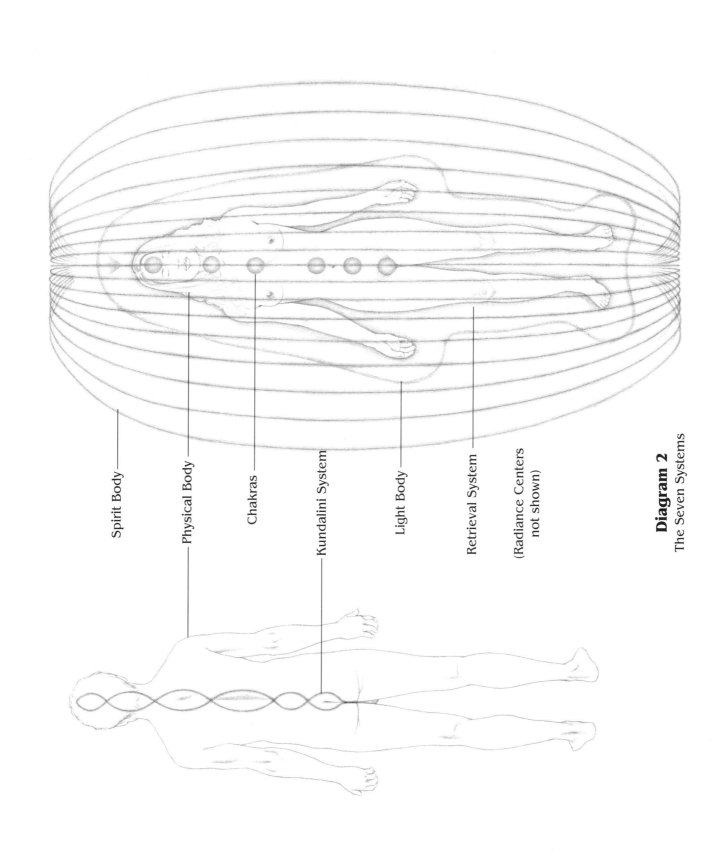

Spirit Body

Physical Body

Chakras

Kundalini System

Light Body

Retrieval System

(Radiance Centers
not shown)

Diagram 2
The Seven Systems

descriptions/interpretations
by different teachers/writers
of energy and subtle energy systems)
Most of the descriptions in this framework
are more likely
to describe a situation
at the end of puberty,
which is probably the best common-denominator phase
for conveying a static view
of complex, dynamic processes

What follows is
a theoretical model,
a conceptual framework,
a paradigm
for some of us some of the time
describing what a human being is / potentially can be
describing what orgasm is / potentially can be
What follows
is only another set of signposts

9. The Seven Systems

What we call a human being
is more than a physical body
In *Sacred Orgasms*
what we are
is a more-or-less integration
of several systems

Some of the systems
at least some of the time
appear as a shape similar to a physical body
Some have no semblance to a body shape
This is why the word *system*
rather than *body*
(Also there are emanations,
or energetic fields,
around the different systems,
though these emanations are not discussed)
A system is a *system*
partly because it is a different structure
partly because it has a different function(s)
but mainly because it is made up of and/or utilizes
a different form of energy or combination of energies
than the other systems
Even more important for *Sacred Orgasms,*
orgasms in the different systems
feel different, generally
Delineating and describing the different systems
is the best way I know
to understand all of a diverse set of phenomena
as *orgasm*

THE PHYSICAL BODY

Easily conceived of as a system,
    the physical body has a structure of
        muscles, bones, nerves, arteries, veins, organs, glands,
        and so on

The physical body's source of energy comes basically,
        directly or indirectly from plant life,
    carrying transformed sunlight
        which is one form of
        physical energy,
            as I will term
            one of four general categories of energy
            used by the seven systems

The physical body orgasm
        is as defined earlier:
    a muscular tension/contractions/release cycle
        usually but not always by stimulation of
        the clitoris, head of penis, G-spot, and/or prostate gland
    sometimes with, sometimes without ejaculation
The personal experience
        of a physical body orgasm
    can be far, far more varied
        than this definition implies
    Moreover, in conjunction with a physical body orgasm,
        there can be orgasms
            in the subtle energy systems
            or in parts/subsystems of these subtle energy systems
    This is what makes
        each orgasm experience unique

The physical body is
        what we live with in the physical world
    Obviously, we would have little effect
        in the physical world
        without a physical body
For the subtle energy systems,
        obvious no longer applies
    Unfortunately, without obvious, observable, discernible
            objects or events
        we can slip easily into woo-woo land
    Woo-woo is *not* another spiritual, Eastern term
        like wu-wei
    Woo-woo
        is nomenclature for
            spaced-out
            ungrounded
            unfounded
            non-reality
I have wondered/worried
        if all this is a woo-woo paradigm
It was my own orgasms, however,
            —the *consistent* patterns
                of different orgasmic experiences
            (the sensations are real!)

that kept bringing me back to
"maybe the paradigm is valid"

THE CHAKRAS

The chakras are another
            coexisting system
Unlike two physical objects
            such as a hand and a table
      that cannot occupy
            the same space at the same time,
      the chakras and the other subtle energy systems
            can, in a loose sense, occupy
            the same space at the same time
                  with each other
                  as well as with physical objects
      Better than *occupy*,
            we might say
            interwoven or *interspersed* or *interpenetrating*

Chakras, probably,
      are the most described / discussed / pursued after
      of the subtle energy systems
      in esoteric/mystical/metaphysical/spiritual traditions

As in the tantra discussion earlier,
            there are seven principal chakras
      Each chakra is
            a single spinning vortex, initially
            In later stages of development
                  some of the chakras
                  are two or three spinning vortexes
      The spinning vortex has an appearance
            sort of like a cone
                  tapering to a rounded end
                  at the smaller end
      Personally, I am more likely to *feel*
            the smaller ends
                  which are the area of energetic focalization
            and are more or less along the core of, *inside* of
                  the physical body
            from just above the anus
            to just beneath the top of the head
      In later stages of development
            there are at least ten principal chakras
                        perhaps sixteen
                  some *above* the head
                  some *below* the pelvis

Chakras, in a sense,
      are the digestion system
      for the other subtle energy systems
            at least until puberty
The main function of the chakras
            most of the time for most of us

My vineyard is mine to give;
my fruit is mine to give
Song of Songs

is to transform/convert/transubstantiate/transmute
physical energy
into other usable forms of energy
for the other subtle energy systems

Each principal chakra is capable of having an orgasm
For me, a single-chakra orgasm
is like fireworks viewed from a distance
The sensation is a soft glow
expanding outward
from its center
fading gently into the night sky
When the orgasm is
multiple-chakra and/or multiple-system,
the sensations are blended/mixed together
into a whole
greater than the sum of its parts
with multiple sensation patterns possible

THE KUNDALINI SYSTEM

Kundalini (pronounced *coon dah lee´ nee*)
like *chakra*
is another word from Sanskrit
Kundalini, the term, is used many different ways
and in the West
the kundalini system is often confused
with the chakra system
Both the seven principal chakras and the kundalini system
are along the midline of the body
Both systems' main function
is to transform physical energy
into forms of energy
usable by other subtle energy systems

Their structures, however,
are very different
The kundalini system,
as I am using the term here,
is a continuous current of energy
ascending and descending in two wave-like patterns,
basically along the spinal column
In the coccyx, the current is a single branch
Similar to the shape of the caduceus,
an emblem of the Western medical profession,
the ascending and descending flow of the current intersects
at each of the seven principal chakras
Here at each intersection
a tiny current connects with
the small, rounded cone end of the nearby chakra vortex
This is one of the ways,
through the kundalini system,
the chakras
are in communication with each other
It is also via these tiny currents

that the kundalini system
obtains from the chakras
the transformed physical energy
which the kundalini system then transforms
into what I term here as *spiritual energy,* or the *life force,*
or what some teachers/writers sometimes call
kundalini energy

This transformation of physical energy
into spiritual energy
is basically ongoing
During a kundalini system orgasm, however,
a major quantity of spiritual energy
is transformed
For me,
a kundalini orgasm
is a burst of energy
in the dome of the head
When such an orgasm occurs in conjunction
with an orgasm
in either of the two chakras *located* in the head area,
there is an *explosion*
experienced in the head area
The *burst*
can be *blinding* to all conscious awarenesses
Sounds, sights, and feelings disappear
The feeling is sort of like *passing out* from hyperventilation
but is definitely a different phenomenon
When I *come back,*
there is a freshness, a calmness, a contentment

THE RETRIEVAL SYSTEM

The Retrieval System is actually a shortened version
of a more descriptive title:
the auric memory storage and retrieval system
Taking the shape of an aura surrounding the physical form
this system appears as a soft, white-light glow
usually from *inside* the area just beneath the skin
to outside the physical body about half an inch
except during specific functions
when the glow extends *outward* to about a foot

The retrieval system's main function is to serve as
a storehouse of information:
thoughts, inner images,
sensations, feelings, emotions
—all these are experiences
which we can conceptualize as being
both mental and emotional energies
some experiences being more mental
some experiences being more emotional
Using physical energy
transformed by the chakras,
the retrieval system

codifies the informational aspect
usually leaving the emotional energies
and the remaining mental energies to flow freely
Then as needed,
this system can access and retrieve
the information if, and this is a major "if,"
the emotional blockage/repression/suppression does not interfere

A retrieval system orgasm, for me, is
soft, pleasurable waves
flowing throughout the whole of this *body*
—pure pleasure in almost stillness

THE LIGHT BODY

This system is called the light body
because when *seen*
it looks like a body of light

Comparable to the retrieval system,
the light body has a similar exterior shape
as the physical body
The light body, however,
is brighter,
extends several inches exterior to the retrieval system,
and permeates the physical body throughout
Unlike the retrieval system's soft white glow,
the light body projects colors,
the color of which depending on
at least to some extent
the mental/emotional tone of the retrieval system
Some clairvoyants call these colors the aura
—another example of the same term
meaning different things/directions

Inside the physical body,
the light body flows through
a vast network of minute channels
some of which
are what we call the acupuncture meridians
as well as what the tantric tradition
calls *nadis* (pronounced *nah´ dees*)
of which there are about 72,000
according to yogic texts

The light body's principal function
is to carry what many of us call the *life-force*
(or what I am terming *spiritual energy*)
throughout the physical body
Often what some of us term a *full-body orgasm*
is a very intense flow of this life-force
through many of the channels in the physical body
as a result of a physical body orgasm
in conjunction
with a kundalini and chakra orgasm

Some day, after we have mastered the winds, the waves, the tides and gravity, we shall harness for God the energies of love. Then for the second time in the history of the world, man will have discovered fire.

Teilhard de Chardin

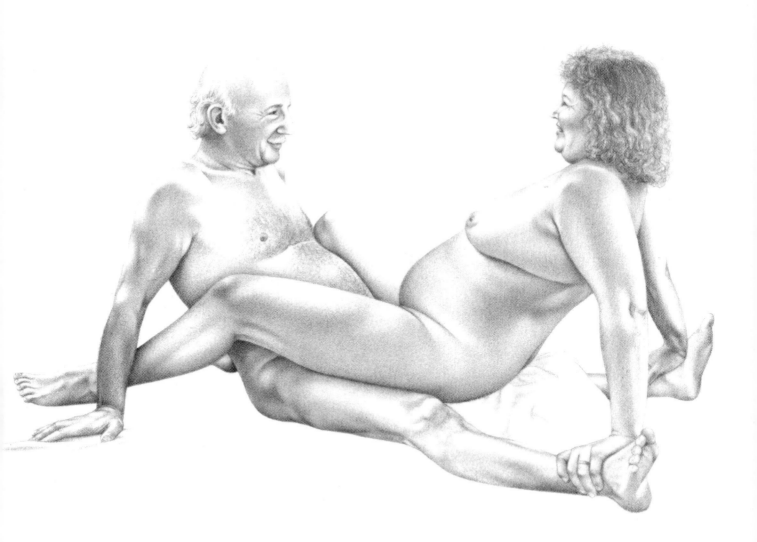

Probably some of us experience orgasms
like this all of the time
Thus, *full-body* makes sense only if
we also have non-full-body orgasms

When there is an orgasm in the light body only,
for me,
there is a pleasurable electric-shock-like sensation
usually causing extensive movement
in the physical body

The light body serves two additional,
sometimes critical, functions:
what we might call *extraordinary endurance*
and *extraordinary strength*
We wonder how in *heroic rescues*
or other emergencies
the muscles can work far longer
and/or far more powerfully
than in the usual everyday life
It is probably the light body
that has been
tapped into / utilized / drawn upon

In later stages of development
this is the system that has what shamans
sometimes call the *luminous egg* or *luminous sphere*
and the *fibres* that we can *shoot*/extend
from our navel area

THE SPIRIT BODY

Generally, the system encompassing,
in an oval-like shape,
all the other systems
is what I term the *spirit body*
or we could say the *astral body*

There are two main functions
of the spirit body
When there is an orgasm,
any kind of orgasm in any system,
there is an energy generated,
sort of a primordial energy,
which can be easily transformed
by any of the other systems
for use by that particular system
It is in the spirit body
that any untransformed primordial energy
is temporarily *suspended*

The second main function of the spirit body
concerns any mental energy and emotional energy
which became *stuck* in the retrieval system

Sometimes, after the retrieval system
            has sort of extracted
the informational aspect of an experience,
            the emotional energy remains *attached*
                        to the codified mental energy,
                as in the grasping and avoiding of attachments
                        from the tantra teachings
It is during orgasm
                of any system(s)
            that the spirit body *unsticks*
                        in conjunction with the light body
                at least some of the attachments
This is the *how*
                in the why
                        most of us most of the time
                are so emotionally content
                        after an orgasm
The sometimes tears and crying
                        after an orgasm
                are rarely due to sadness and grief
                during lovemaking or masturbation
The bursting out in laughter
                here is not from a joke
These are emotional releases
                which the spirit body facilitates
To some extent,
            the more intense the orgasm,
            the more the emotional clearing
And for some of us some of the time
            the main emotional releasing
            does not occur until
            the *final one* in a series of orgasms

As for a spirit-body orgasm itself
    here the sensations
                are very subtle, sort of etheric
The orgasm could be very easily missed
                if we are not looking for it
However, since the spirit body is usually the principal system
                in *astral projections*, or *out-of-the-body* experiences,
                (when an individual
                        for example
                is suddenly viewing their own physical body
                        from *outside* their physical body
                or sometimes when a dream is vividly real
                        even to the extent it does not *feel* like a dream)
    it is through astral projections
            that at least some of our "long-distance sex"
            with others occurs

THE RADIANCE CENTERS

The six systems presented thus far
    are all functioning at least to some degree
    within a few weeks after birth

for most of us
It is not until puberty
that we can develop a seventh system
here termed the radiance centers
Most of us never actually develop them
The only other conceptual reference
to such a system
that I have found
is in the Quodoushka teachings

The radiance centers,
of which there can be at least ten,
appear basically the same as chakras
Unlike the more-or-less stationary chakras,
the radiance centers
move throughout the other six systems

The radiance centers' principal function,
similar to the chakras',
is transformation of energies
into energy forms that the other subtle energy systems
can utilize
The radiance centers, however,
can transform a far wider range of energies
—energies that are around us all of the time,
such as energy from crystals,
from certain light and sound waves, and more
Once the radiance centers develop and are functioning,
the chakras are then free
to fulfill other valuable functions

When there is an orgasm in
an individual radiance center only,
the orgasm is probably never felt

When all the radiance centers
have an orgasm together,
they move to
above the top of the head
and form what we would call
a halo
just as we see sometimes depicted above Jesus' head

10. Orgasm

As we shift
if we choose to shift
to a point of view that
we are not only a physical body,
our definition/model of orgasm
might shift as well

Sexual orgasm can be

Sex has been called the original sin
—it is neither original nor sin

Osho

a special, wonderful experience

Sexual orgasm can also be
a teacher
a prototype
an indication
of what orgasm *in general* is like

A physiological definition, however,
does not explain
some of the out-of-the-ordinary orgasms

I propose a broader definition
(in the social sciences
we would say a *conceptual definition*
rather than an *operational definition*):

Orgasm
is two (or more) forms of energy coming together
generating a third energy

I would call my definition an
energy generation model
of orgasm
in contrast to the *tension release* model

Applying the broad, conceptual definition of orgasm
to the physical body only,
the two *forms* are
the nervous system and the hormonal system
Usually, it is the physical
contact/pressure/movement
on the clitoris, head of penis, G-spot, and/or prostate gland
that stimulates the nervous and hormonal systems
to interact, to *come together*,
in a way that results in orgasm

For the subtle energy systems
the two (or more) *forms* of energy could be
two of the *systems* just discussed,
two *sub-systems* within a system
or between two systems,
or a *sub-system* and a *system*

Theoretically
there are many possible
combinations and permutations
between two or more forms
of the physical body and/or subtle energy systems
of ourself with ourself, with another/others
physically touching, physically close but not touching,
physically distant

But why have an orgasm anyway?
regardless of the possible combinations and permutations
regardless if they are *ordinary* or *out-of-the-ordinary* orgasms

In this paradigm
that proposes a human being

is a physical body functioning in conjunction
with several subtle energy systems,
each orgasm has at least three functions/effects
(not *goals*)
regardless of which forms of energy come together
regardless of which system(s) has/have the orgasm

The first function of an orgasm
that most of us would think of is
pleasure
Not only physical pleasure, though
Orgasms can also be
emotionally satisfying
mentally stimulating
and spiritually fulfilling
All this is dependent
at least to some extent
on consensuality
on no mitigating health conditions
and no mitigating emotional conditions
such as dishonest communications

A second function of orgasm
is the generation of energy,
as presented earlier
We could call it *primordial energy*
since all of the subtle energy systems
can easily transform the primordial form
into a form easily usable
by that particular system
Perhaps what is most important about this
primordial energy
is that we generate it
from ourself
within ourself
And why is this important?
Because the underlying function of each system is
health
In orgasm
we generate a resource
to better heal ourself
physically and emotionally

A third function,
which would be rather esoteric
for most of us,
is to integrate
—slowly—
the seven systems
into a single, unified system
This is when we can transform energy at will

11. Transformation

Throughout *Sacred Orgasms*
  the term *transformation*
  is used in various ways

Basically in this paradigm
  transformation means
      the converting of one form of energy
      into another form of energy
          that one or more of the seven systems can use
  The physical body digests/converts/transforms
      food into physical energy
  The chakras digest/convert/transform
      physical energy into forms of energy
      that other subtle energy systems can use
  The kundalini system digests/converts/transforms
      physical energy into spiritual energy
          which is the energy that composes
          most of the spirit body
  And so on

More central to *Sacred Orgasms*
      is a particular type of transformation:
  Under the section on tantra,
      we examined *attachment*
          —our emotional grasping and avoiding nature
  Under the Taoist tradition
      we explored non-attachment
          conceived of as yielding and wu wei
  In the Quodoushka tradition
      being able to live life from any position on the wheel
          is non-attachment
  Under contemporary meditation,
      hands touching our body
          encouraging/facilitating/allowing
          blocked/repressed/suppressed feelings/emotions
              to release
          —this is going from attachment to non-attachment

Among the seven systems,
  it is the retrieval system
      that transforms our experience of the whole
      into two parts: mental energy and emotional energy
  However, after their digestion/conversion
      the two energies sometimes remain attached
  Then, as more and more mental and emotional energies
      remain *stuck together*,
              as more attachment occurs,
          density develops
      Psychologically, we speak of
              "pushing someone's button"
              (pushing someone's density)
          we speak of someone's ego
              —the part of us that is egotistical
  In the musculature
      we speak of body armoring

O Lord, give me chastity and continence
but not yet

St. Augustine

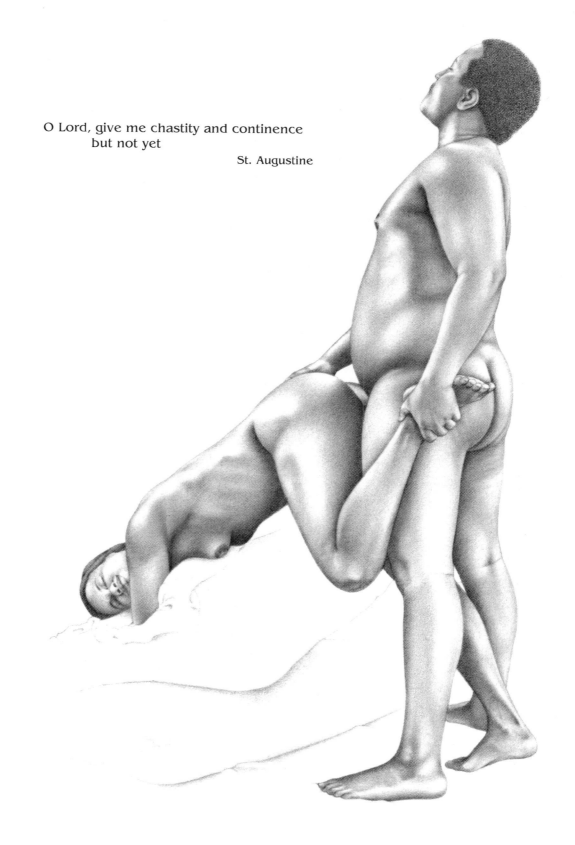

Potentially, there is a major impact on our health
            as the attached energies become
            more and more dense,
                        as they have a tendency to do
Density
            limits / slows down / constricts / restricts
      the *flow* of energy
            in both the physical body
            and its energetic double, the light body
      Density, eventually, results in
            dis-ease and illness
                        in varying degrees in various ways
      During orgasm,
            the spirit body transforms the stuckness,
                        transforms the attachment,
            in a way that separates the emotional energy
            from the mental energy
      Orgasm, in a sense,
            dissolves the density
      This happens during physical body orgasms
            but more so with other types of orgasms
            that might not extensively involve
                        the physical body
Thus, basically, generally,
      orgasms mean greater health
But why are they sacred?

Sacred Orgasms uses the words
      spirit body
There is a reason
      The spirit body, itself,
            functions
                        in a way that most of us would term *spiritual*
            Dissolving the ego
                        (or *dense energy*, as termed earlier)
                  has long been a central spiritual teaching
                        in many traditions
                  We do not enter the king/queendom of heaven
                        until we can be born again,
                        until we can be as newborn infants:
                              egoless
      The ego (me! mine! I!)
            is a major stumbling block
                  along spiritual paths
      Energetically speaking,
                  in everyday life
            the spirit body is too tied up
                  dissolving the ego
                  transforming stuck energies
            to develop itself further
      In orgasm
                  especially in kundalini orgasm
            more spiritual energy is created
                  (*spiritual energy* is not holier,
                        just *of-the-spirit-body*)
      In orgasm
            the spirit body transforms

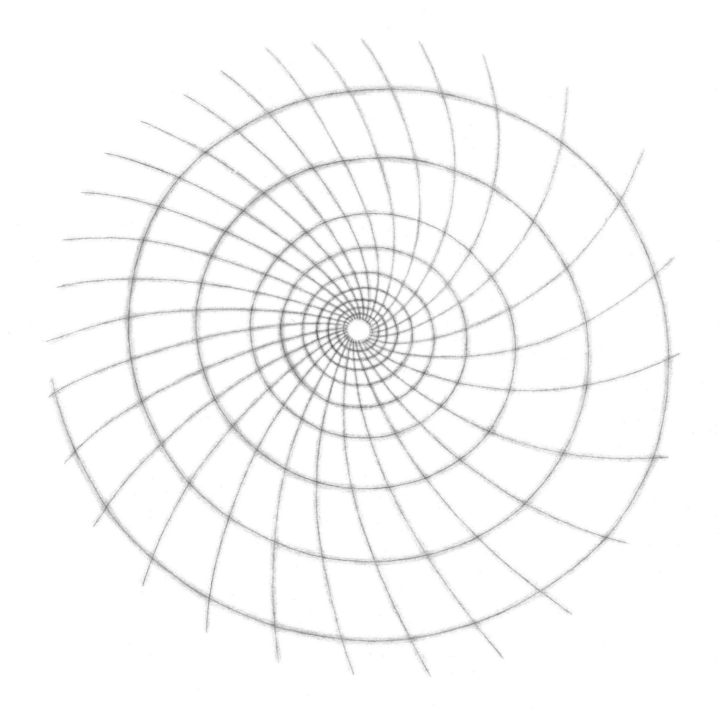

Diagram 3
Wisdom Center in Orgasmic State

more/faster
stuck mental/emotional energies

Additionally, with more spiritual energy, our spirit body is able
to bring in / develop
what we might call
our spiritual dimensions, our *wisdom centers*
or collectively, our *Higher Self*
These centers can appear as radiant, sphere-like shapes
often *occupying* the same space
as the principal chakras
(Some orgasms in these centers feel similar
to a kundalini orgasm)
From these wisdom centers
we are able to deepen our understanding
of the nature of our existence
of the Great Spirit, of God/ess
Here we come to experience
unconditional love
consciousness
space
time
knowledge
This is why orgasm
is sacred:
through orgasm
eventually, potentially
we are able
to connect with our inner wisdom
With orgasm
our own orgasm
within ourself
we can transcend our everyday mind
our everyday existence
we can become/be
our expanded self
our transcended self
we can BE
This is why sex
can be considered
a path to enlightenment
(not necessarily the best path
for all of us all of the time):
Sex,
with ourself, with others,
potentially
brings us to orgasm,
usually to what we might call sexual orgasm
Sexual orgasm,
if we are attentive
and open to going beyond cultural limitations,
potentially
brings us
to an awareness of energy
An awareness of energy
sometimes with the knowledge of spiritual traditions

This is my body which speaks for itself...
This is my body which sings of itself
James Broughton, *Song of the Godbody*

potentially
brings us to other forms
of energetic development
Energetic development
potentially
brings us to spiritual wisdom
and potentially
brings us to other forms of orgasm
which in turn can bring us to more energetic development
which in turn can bring us to more spiritual wisdom
It is all, potentially, a beautifully expanding spiral

Both in orgasm and in wisdom
neither the spirit nor the flesh is superior
Rather, they are mutually enhancing

This is where *Sacred Orgasms* began:
To the extent
we deny our spiritual nature,
we limit our sexual nature
To the extent
we deny our sexual nature,
we limit our spiritual nature

One of my principal teachers,
a Tibetan lama,
in response to one of my questions,
turned to me
and said,
looking directly into my eyes,
"You know,
you already have it all
within you."

Additional Reading/Viewing

Books

Ecstasy Through Tantra, Dr. Jonn Mumford, Llewellyn Publications, St. Paul

Erotic Massage (with 2-volume video), Kenneth Ray Stubbs, Ph.D., Secret Garden, Larkspur, California

Jewel in the Lotus (with 3-volume video), Sunyata Saraswati and Bodhi Avinasha, Kriya Jyoti Tantra Society, San Francisco

Sacred Mirrors, Alex Grey, Inner Traditions, Rochester, Vermont

Sexual Energy Ecstasy, David and Ellen Ramsdale, Peak Skill Publishing, San Diego

Sexual Secrets, Nik Douglas and Penny Slinger, Destiny Books, New York

The Art of Sexual Ecstasy, Margo Anand, Tarcher, Los Angeles

The Eastern Way of Love, Kamala Devi, Simon and Schuster, New York

The Sweet Medicine Sundance Teachings of the Chuluaqui-Quodoushka, Harley SwiftDeer Reagan, Ph.D., Elizabeth Chandra, M.D., and Justin Anthony Murphy. Available only if attending a Quodoushka seminar; contact The Deer Tribe Metis Medicine Society, P.O. Box 1519, Temple City, California 91780

The Tao of Sexology, Dr. Stephen T. Chang, Tao Publishing, San Francisco

Magazines

Ecstasy: The Journal of Divine Eroticism, 402 W. Matilija, Ojai, California 92023

Tantra: The Magazine, P.O. Box 79, Torreon, New Mexico 87061

Videos

Erotic Massage, 2 volumes with accompanying book (see above), Kenneth Ray Stubbs, Ph.D., Secret Garden, P.O. Box 67–SCA, Larkspur, California 94977–0067

Jewel in the Lotus, 3 volumes with accompanying book (see above), Sunyata Saraswati and Bodhi Avinasha, Kriya Jyoti Tantra Society, 633 Post St., San Francisco, California 94109

Tantra Love, David and Ellen Ramsdale with Kevin Kreisler, M.D., Peak Skill Publishing, P.O. Box 5489, Playa Del Rey, California 90296

In Memoriam
1986
Show Me!
by Will McBride
one of the most beautiful spiritual sexuality books ever

censored by the United States justice system

WANTED:
YOUR
EXPERIENCES

Dear Reader:

Very little is known and written about what I call out-of-the-ordinary orgasms. In _Sacred Orgasms_ I share my experiences. We all would benefit if others shared theirs.

In continuing my research for a future book, I invite you to send your descriptions of your own out-of-the-ordinary (or energetic, or mystical) orgasmic experiences.

Include, if you wish, the circumstances, the sensations, the feelings/emotions, the meaning to you, and other relevant information. Some or all of the description, without remuneration, might be quoted in the book, and your anonymity is guaranteed.

Please write to me at:

Secret Garden Publishing
P.O. Box 67-PER
Larkspur, CA 94977-0067

I greatly appreciate your support and interest.

Sincerely,

Ray

Kenneth Ray Stubbs, Ph.D.